Contents

At the vet's
Focus on: v as in _v__an_ 3

Hugs
Focus on: ve as in _ha__ve__ 8

Fun in the mud
Focus on: o as in _s__o__n_ 13

Wet
Focus on: w as in _w__ig_ 18

Scan to listen along!

Audio to accompany this book can be streamed online with a mobile or tablet using this QR code:

About this book

These short stories are designed to give young children blending and reading practice. They are decodable, which means the words in them only include letter shapes and sounds that the children have learned. The stories also gradually introduce a few 'tricky' words, which are essential for children to become familiar with, such as 'they', 'of' and 'said'.

As children progress through these readers, new letter sounds and 'tricky' words are added and previous learning is revised. The progression links directly to the teaching order and lessons in the Letterland *Teacher's Guides* (UK and US versions). Each story begins with a title page that provides important information for children and teachers.

Basic teaching tips:

- Encourage the sounding out of decodable words (and any decodable parts of 'tricky' words).
- Discuss the stories with the children to ensure comprehension and engagement.
- Encourage re-reading in pairs or individually to develop fluency and reading for meaning.

See **www.letterland.com/Phonics-Readers** and the latest editions of the Letterland **Teacher's Guides** for more suggestions on how to use this book.

At the vet's

Tricky word: here

Focus on: v as in <u>v</u>an

Here is the vet's van. It has a dog, a cat and a duck in it.

I'll go in here with this dog and cat. Then I'll be back.

I go into the vet's with a duck.
It has a bad wing.

Here is my Mum. She is the vet!
That is her job and I help her.

Hugs

Tricky word: too

Focus on: ve as in *ha<u>ve</u>*

Let me give you a bib.

I *have* a bib, Mum!

Let me give you a cup.

I *have* a cup, too!

Let me give you a dish.

I *have* a dish, too!

Let me give you a hug.

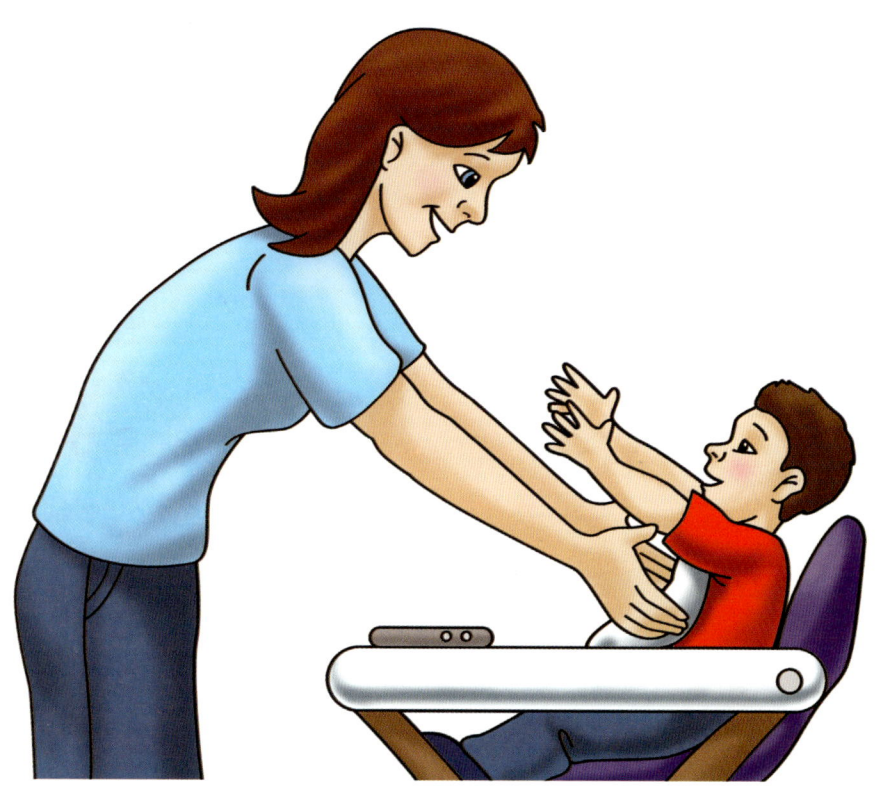

Give me *lots* of hugs
and a kiss, too, Mum!

Fun in the mud

Focus on: o as in *s<u>o</u>n*

He spins in some mud.
He is wet. He is a mess.

Come along, son, but not in here. Too much mud!

Wet

Tricky word: said

Focus on: w as in *wig*

"I love to get them wet!"
he said.

Here is a wet pup. "I love to wag, wag, wag," he said.

"I love to flap, flap, flap," the duck said.

"I wish this web was not wet," she said.

About this series

This series consists of 20 books which are divided into four sets. Each book contains a selection of short stories, featuring the phonic elements listed below. In total there are 83 engaging stories that children can use to decode the 44 sounds of the English language. For more information, see **www.letterland.com/Phonics-Readers**

Set	Book	No. of stories	Focus elements	As in the word...
1	a	4	c, a, d, h, m, t, s, i, s	cat, add, dog, hen, map, tap, sun, it, is
	b	4	i, i, n, g	it, ice, net, go
	c	4	o, o, p, s, s	odd, so, pen, cats, dogs
	d	4	e, e, ss, u	egg, he, miss, up
	e	4	u, k, ck, ng	uniform, kit, duck, ring
2	a	4	sh, ch, th, th	shop, chip, that, thing
	b	4	l, f, ff, ll, b	leg, fan, puff, bell, bat
	c	4	j, all, r, qu	jet, ball, run, quiz
	d	4	v, ve, o, w	van, have, son, wig
	e	4	x, y, z	box, yes, zip
3	a	5	sl, sp, st, sw, sk, sm, sn, cl, fl, pl, bl, gl, br, cr, dr, fr, gr, tr	slip, spot, stuck, swim, skate, smash, snap, clock, flag, plug, block, glad, brick, crab, drip, frog, grin, track
	b	4	cr, dr, fr, gr, nd, nk, nt, y	crab, drip, frog, grin, hand, tank, tent, my
	c	5	a_e, i_e, e_e, o_e, u_e, ed, ed, ed	make, like, these, home, cube, skated, smiled, hoped
	d	4	ed, ed, ed, y, ai, ay, ee	landed, clapped, slammed, baby, rain, say, bee
	e	4	ea, oa, ie, ue	sea, boat, tie, blue
4	a	4	ild, ind, old, ar, or	mild, kind, cold, farm, for
	b	3	ir, ur, er	girl, fur, her
	c	4	ow, igh	show, night
	d	4	oo, oo, u, aw, au, ew, ew	moon, book, put, saw, cause, few, grew
	e	6	ow, ou, oy, oi, air, ear	how, out, boy, coin, fair, year

Titles in this series

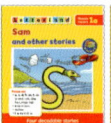 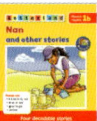   

Set 1
- Sam and other stories
- Nat and other stories
- Go, pup, go! and other stories
- Pets and other stories
- Can he kick? and other stories

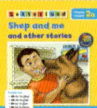    

Set 2
- Shep and me and other stories
- Is this her pet? and other stories
- Red Robot runs and other stories
- Hugs and other stories
- Zig and Zag and other stories

Set 3
- Spin and smash and other stories
- Can a crab grab? and other stories
- Rose bakes a cake and other stories
- Look what happened! and other stories
- Molly and me by the sea and other stories

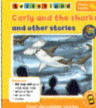    

Set 4
- Carly and the sharks and other stories
- My very bad morning and other stories
- Ben's birthday surprise and other stories
- Penguins on the loose and other stories
- What big flippers you have and other stories

Published by Letterland International Ltd. 8/10 South Street, Epsom, Surrey, KT18 7PF, UK
© Letterland International 2013. Reprinted 2017, 2018, 2019, 2020, 2021.
10 9 8 7

Sold as part of Set 2. ISBN: 978-1-86209-892-3, Product Code: TE11
This book ISBN: 978-1-86209-903-6, Product Code: TE22
LETTERLAND™ is a trademark of Letterland International Ltd.
Printed in China

Author: Stamey Carter
Editor: Lyn Wendon
Originator of Letterland: Lyn Wendon
Artwork: Baz Rowell
Design: Beth Maddox

The author asserts the moral right to be identified as the author of this work.
All rights reserved. No part of this publication may be reproduced, stored in a retrieval system, or transmitted in any form or by any means, electronic, mechanical, photocopying, recording or otherwise, without either the prior permission of the Publisher or a licence permitting restricted copying in the United Kingdom issued by the Copyright Licensing Agency Ltd, 90 Tottenham Court Road, London W1T 4LP. This book is sold subject to the condition that it shall not by way of trade or otherwise be lent, hired out or otherwise circulated without the Publisher's prior consent.